Colouring for mindfulness

Vintage

50 designs to help you de-stress

hamlyn

Forget everyday cares and worries!

Be transported back to the simple joys of childhood as you colour in these pretty designs. Do you remember how much pleasure colouring in gave you and how peaceful you would feel? Or if you've ever doodled in the margins of notes or coloured in images in a magazine while chatting on the phone, you'll know it's fun and doesn't require any particular skill. It's a link to the child that you once were and gives you the chance for a quiet pause in the day. And finally, it reawakens the creativity that is in all of us.

When you are feeling stressed, there's nothing like losing yourself in choosing colours and carefully filling in some figurative or abstract shapes. The blank designs are a great way to reboot a brain too occupied with the demands of smartphones and tablets.

In this book you will find 50 designs, all selected because of their power to evoke the pleasures of the past. Just choose one that appeals to you instinctively, at random, and begin.

This book belongs to:

. . . .

. . . .

. . . .

An Hachette UK Company
www.hachette.co.uk

First published in France in 2013 by Dessain et Tolra

This edition published in Great Britain in 2015 by
Hamlyn, a division of Octopus Publishing Group Ltd
Carmelite House
50 Victoria Embankment
London EC4Y 0DZ
www.octopusbooks.co.uk

ISBN 978-0-600-63291-7

A CIP catalogue record for this book is available from the British Library.

Printed and bound in China

10 9 8 7 6

Publishing directors: Isabelle Jeuge-Maynart, Ghislaine Stora
Cover: Claire Morel Fatio, Abigail Read
Layout: Claire Morel Fatio
Senior production manager: Katherine Hockley

There are no rules: use whatever medium you like – felt tips, pencils, gouache, pastels – and whatever colours you like from the selection available. You will gradually feel calmer and soon be completely absorbed in what you are doing and the colours filling up the shapes. Concentrate on the smallest details.

There are also some blank spaces to fill with your own shapes and designs, while some designs have been begun with dotted lines, and it's up to you to complete them, guided by just your imagination and chance. Finally, to help with concentration and meditation, cut out the designs that inspire you the most and contemplate them in a calm environment, allowing your thoughts to roam free.

Just 5 – 10 minutes of colouring a day will help you to relax and find inner peace.

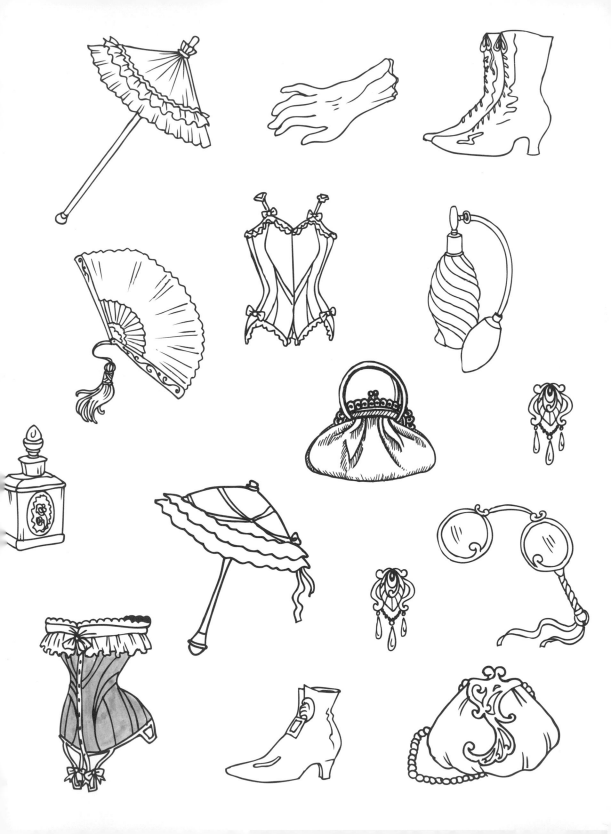

Create as many curls of smoke as you want.

Decorate the cup or imagine the wallpaper behind it.

Continue the lines and create an extraordinary butterfly.

Continue the lines and create all kinds of facades.

Create wallpaper with a foliage pattern.

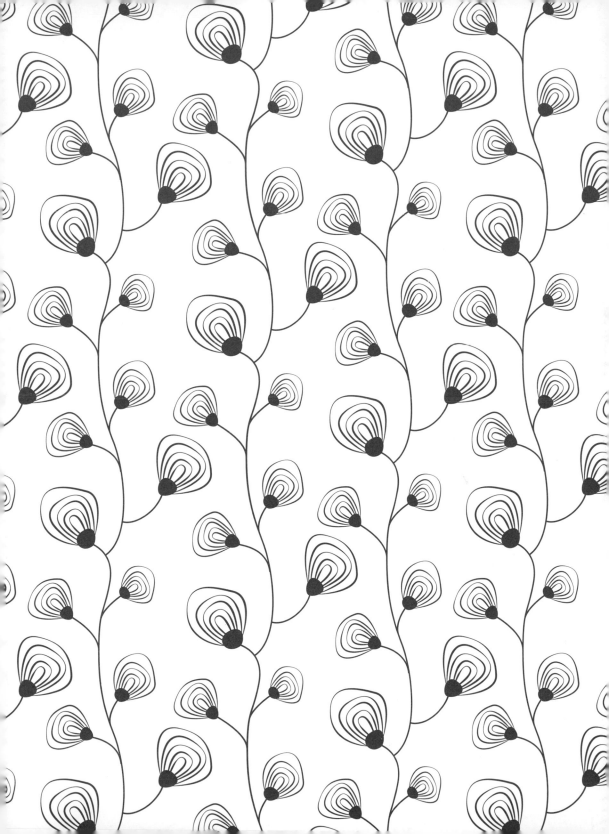

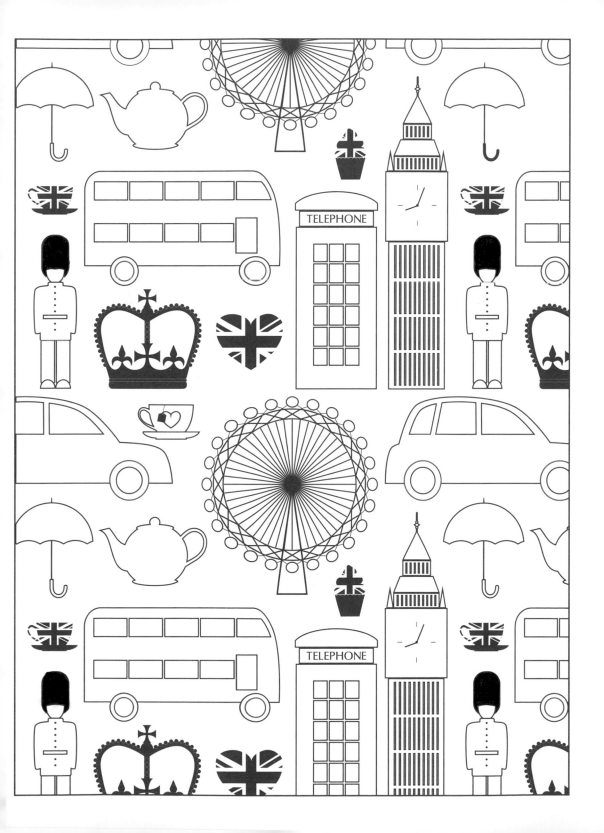

Fill this heart with floral details.

Decorate these balls or create a wallpaper.